This book contains a host of pictures
of things, people, and beasts, many
of which you have seen again and again.
Can you identify these pictures by name?

This is a great book for a social
gathering, and will evoke an endless
stream of comment. Nostalgia and
association will turn these games into
great fun and very stimulating
entertainment.

NAME IT!

MARK B. BANDERLY

A HART BOOK

A & W VISUAL LIBRARY • NEW YORK

PUBLISHED BY
A&W PUBLISHERS, INC.
95 MADISON AVENUE
NEW YORK, NEW YORK 10016

ISBN: 0-89104-145-1

PRINTED IN THE UNITED STATES OF AMERICA

CONTENTS

NAME IT!

THEY ALL BEGIN WITH C

Below you will find 10 objects, all of which begin with the letter C. The number of letters in each object is shown by the number of dashes underneath the picture. How many of these pictures can you identify?

A score of 4 is good; 6 is above average; and 9 is just super.

Answers on page 114

1. _ _ _ _ _ _ _

2. _ _ _ _ _ _

3. _ _ _ _ _ _ _ _ _ _ _

4. _ _ _ _ _ _ _ _

5. _ _ _ _ _ _ _

6. _ _ _ _ _ _ _ _ _ _ _ _

7. _ _ _ _ _ _

8. _ _ _ _ _ _ _

9. _ _ _ _ _ _ _ _ _

10. _ _ _ _ _ _

THEY ALL BEGIN WITH F

Below, you will find 11 objects, all of which begin with the letter F. The number of letters in each object is shown by the number of dashes underneath the picture. How many of these pictures can you identify?

A score of 4 is good; 5 is above average; and 8 is remarkable.

Answers on page 114

1. _ _ _ _ _ _ _

2. _ _ _ _

3. _ _ _ _ _ _

4. _ _ _ _

5. _ _ _ _ _

6. _ _ _ _ _ _ _

7. _ _ _ _ _ _ _

8. _ _ _ _

9. _ _ _ _ _ _ _ _ _

10. _ _ _ _ _ _ _

11. _ _ _ _ _ _

11

THEY ALL BEGIN WITH H

Each of the 9 items below begins with the letter H. The dashes beneath each picture indicate the number of letters in the name. How many can you identify?

A score of 5 is not half-bad; 7 or more is honorific.

Answers on page 114

1. _ _ _ _ _

2. _ _ _ _ _ _ _

3. _ _ _ _ _

4. _ _ _ _ _ _ _

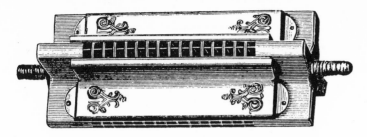

5. _ _ _ _ _ _ _ _ _

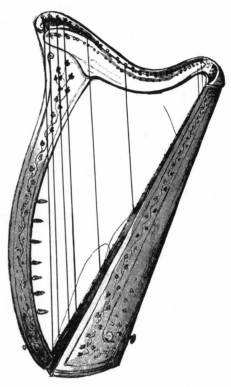

6. _ _ _ _ _

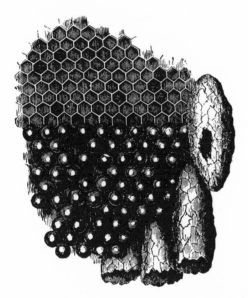

7. _ _ _ _ _ _ _ _ _

8. _ _ _ _ _ _

9. _ _ _ _ _ _ _

SIGNIFICANT INSIGNIA

Here are 17 insignia representing various corporations and societies. Some you will recognize readily, and some will require a little more concentration. The dashes under each symbol indicate the number of letters in the name of the organization. How many can you identify?

A score of 7 is good; 9 is excellent; and 11 signifies superior powers of observation.

Answers on page 114

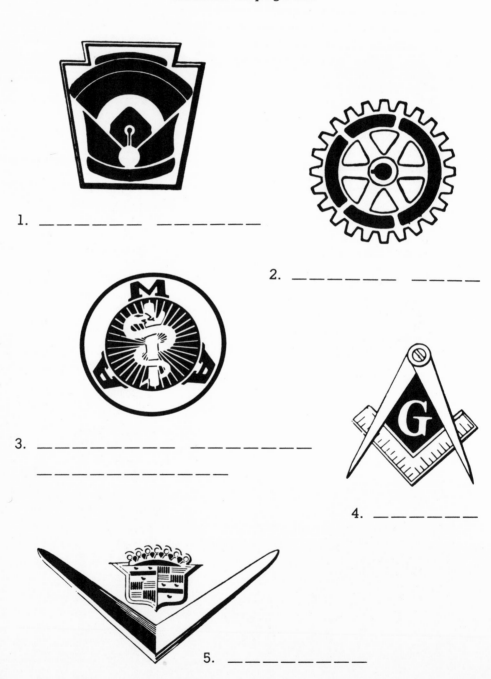

1. _ _ _ _ _ _ _   _ _ _ _ _ _ _

2. _ _ _ _ _ _ _   _ _ _ _ _

3. _ _ _ _ _ _ _ _   _ _ _ _ _ _ _ _
   _ _ _ _ _ _ _ _ _ _ _

4. _ _ _ _ _ _

5. _ _ _ _ _ _ _ _ _

6. ____ ____

7. _____

8. _____ _____

_____

9. _____

_____

___ ___

_____

__ _____

_____

10. _____ _____

12. _____ ____'_

_____

_____

11. ____ _____

__ _____

13. _ _ _ _ _ _ _ _ _ _ _

    _ _ _ _ _ _ _

14. _ _. _ _ _ _ _ _

    _ _ _ _ _ _ _ _ _

16. _ _ _ _ _ _ _ _ _ _ _ _ _

    _ _ _ _ _ _ _ _ _ _

    _ _ _ _ _ _ _

15. _._. _ _ _ _ _

    _ _ _ _ _

17. _ _ _ _ _ _ _ _ _

THEY ALL BEGIN WITH B

There are 17 pictures below. The names of each of these pictures begins with the letter B. Each dash stands for a letter. How many of these pictures can you recognize?

A score of 6 is good; 12 is far above average; and 14 bellows out that you're a whiz.

Answers on page 114

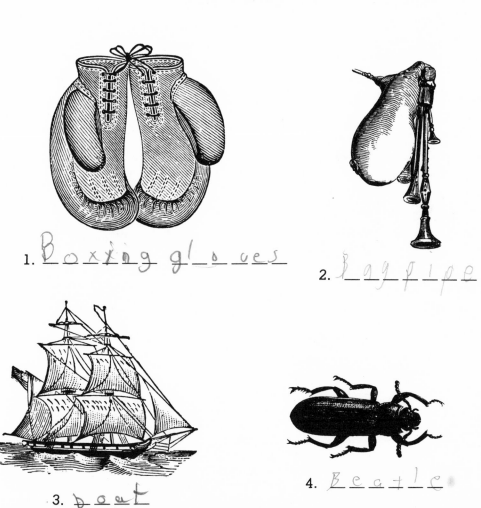

1. <u>Boxing gloves</u>

2. <u>Bagpipe</u>

3. <u>Boat</u>

4. <u>Beatle</u>

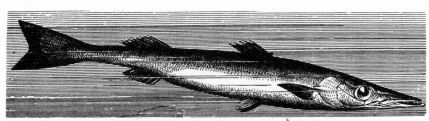

5. <u>barracuda</u>

7. <u>basket</u>

6. <u>breastplate</u>

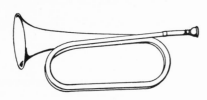

8. <u>bugle</u>

9. <u>balcony</u>

10. <u>bonnet</u>

11. _____

18

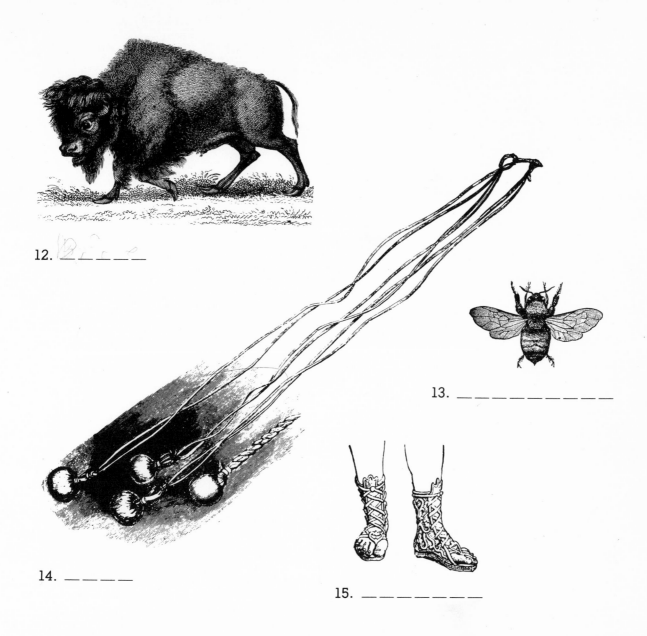

12. _B___ _

13. _ _ _ _ _ _ _ _ _ _

14. _ _ _ _

15. _ _ _ _ _ _ _ _

16. _ _ _ _ _ _ _ _

17. binocklers

19

NOTED ACTRESSES

On these pages, you see the pictures of 10 well-known actresses. Can you recognize them? A hint is given under each name.

A score of 5 is good; 7 is excellent; and a clean sweep merits you a thunderous ovation.

Answers on page 114

Currently Mrs. Warner, the wife of a Virginia senator

1. _____

Romanced Rock Hudson in *Pillow Talk*

2. _____

Star of *Look for the Silver Lining*

3. _____

Called "The Divine," she dominated the 19th-century French stage

4. _____

She taunted Leslie Howard in
Of Human Bondage

5. _____

Bogey's beloved

7. _____

She starred with Charles Boyer
in Algiers

6. _____

Wowed us all in
Some Like It Hot

8. _____

Played the ambitious reporter
in *Network*

9._____

Starred with Hope and
Crosby in the Road series.

10. _____

YE GODS!

Below you will find a gallery of 20 mythological figures, each of which represents a deity. These were the gods of the Greeks, the Hindu Inians, the ancient Egyptians, and the Assyrians. How many of these can you recognize? In order to help, we've put as many dashes underneath the picture as there are in the name you are looking for. Also, the last letter of each name has been provided.

A score of 5 is good; 7 is average; 9 is excellent; 11 is terrific; and 15 is out of sight.

Answers on page 114

1. _ _ _ _ _ _ **N**

2. _ _ _ _ **Y**

3. _ _ _ _ **A**

4. _ _ _ **N**

5. _ _ _ _ _ _ **S**

6. _ _ _ _ **S**

7. _ _ _ _ _ _ _ _ **S**

8. _ _ _ _ **O**

9. _ _ _ _ **S**

10. _ _ _ _ _ _ _ _ **E**

11. _ _ _ _ _ **S**

12. _ _ _ _ _ **S**

13. _ _ _ _ _ _ **A**

14. _ _ _ _ _ **A**

15. _ _ _ _ **R**

16. _ _ _ _ _ _ _ **S**

17. _ _ _ _ _ _ _ **Y**

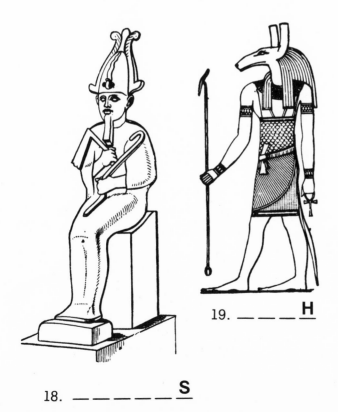

18. _ _ _ _ _ _ **S**

19. _ _ _ _ **H**

20. _ _ _ _ _ _ _ _ **E**

CARRIAGES

There's a special romantic charm associated with taking a trip in a carriage. Pictured on these two pages are 14 carriages—a few are still in use today. The dashes indicate the number of letters in each name. The initial letters have been supplied. How many can you identify?

A score of 2 is average; 5 is very good; 8 is exceptional; 10 means you are a fine student of the good old days.

Answers on page 115

1. C _ _ _ _ _

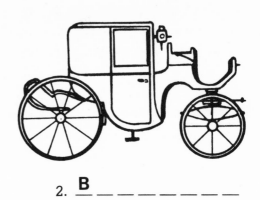

2. B _ _ _ _ _ _ _

3. D _ _ _

4. B _ _ _ _

5. D _ _ _

6. W _ _ _ _ _ _ _ _

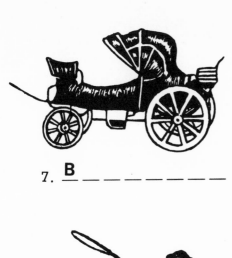

7. **B** _ _ _ _ _ _

8. **T** _ _ _ _ _

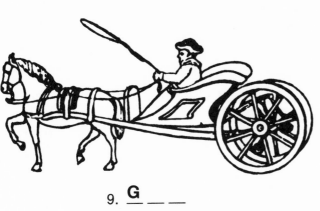

9. **G** _ _ _

10. **R** _ _ _ _ _ _ _ _

11. **D** _ _ _ _ _ _ _ _

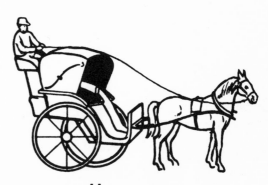

12. **H** _ _ _ _ _

13. **P** _ _ _ _ _ _

14. **C** _ _ _ _ _

EUROPEAN STATESMEN

Here are 16 European statesmen and stateswomen. Can you match their faces to their names? To help you, there are hints under each picture.

A score of 5 is average; 9 is excellent; and 12 is outstanding.

Answers on page 115

Noted British statesman and writer, 1870's.

1. _____

German statesman, he established the Prussian empire.

2. _____

Founder of Communism in Russia.

3. _____

Cardinal. Chief French minister during the reign of the Medicis.

4. _____

Liberal Prime Minister of England during the 19th century.

5. _____

Prime minister of England during World War II.

6. _____

He helped unify Italy.

7. _____

She reigned in England during the 16th century.

8. _____

Irish patriot and prime minister.

9. _____

English Queen, 19th century.

10. _____

Roman ruler and general,
assassinated by his friends.

11. _____

A leader of the Jacobins in the
French Revolution, he instigated
the Reign of Terror.

12. _____

Italian dictator and founder of Fascism.

13. _____

Emperor of France, his
diminutive stature earned
him the nickname,
"The Little Corporal."

14. _____

Communist ruler, noted for
shoe-pounding episode before the
U.N. General Assembly.

15. _____

An enlightened despot, he made Prussia
the foremost military power.

16. _____

SOME SHAPE!

The 22 shapes below are either standard geometric forms or else conventional designs. How many can you name?

A score of 14 is good, 17 is very good, and 20 is exceptional. Only a mathematician by avocation, who is also an architect by profession, could manage to handle them all.

Answers on page 115

1. _ _ _ _ _ _ _ _ _

2. _ _ _ _ _ _ _ _ _

3. _ _ _ _ _ _ _ _ _

4. _ _ _ _ _ _ _ _ _

5. _ _ _ _ _ _ _ _

6. _ _ _ _ _ _ _ _

7. _ _ _ _ _ _ _

8. _ _ _ _ _ _ _ _ _

9. _ _ _ _ _ _ _

10. _ _ _ _ _ _ _ _

11. _ _ _ _ _

12. _ _ _ _ _ _ _ _

13. _ _ _ _ _ _ _ _

14. _ _ _ _ _ _ _ _ _ _ _

15. _ _ _ _ _ _ _ _ _ _ _

16. _ _ _ _ _ _ _

17. _ _ _ _ _

18. _ _ _ _ _ _ _ _ _ _ _ _ _

19. _ _ _ _ _ _ _ _ _ _

20. _ _ _ _ _ _ _ _ _ _ _ _

21. _ _ _ _ _ _ _ _

22. _ _ _ _ _ _

THEY ALL BEGIN WITH L

Below, you will find 9 objects, all of which begin with the letter L. The number of letters in each object is shown by the number of dashes underneath the picture. How many of these pictures can you identify?

A score of 4 is passing; 6 is very good; 7 is excellent; and 8 is exceptional.

Answers on page 115

1. _ _ _ _

2. _ _ _ _ _

3. _ _ _ _ _ _

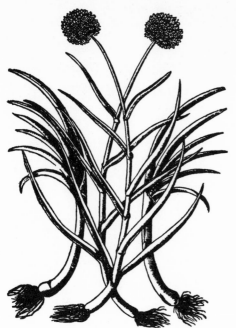

4. _ _ _ _ _

5. _ _ _ _ _ _ _

6. _ _ _ _ _ _

7. _ _ _ _ _ _ _ _ _

8. _ _ _ _ _ _ _

9. _ _ _ _ _ _

35

GREAT STRUCTURES

On the following pages are pictured 13 world-famous structures. Under each picture there is a hint indicating the number of letters in the name of the building. Please identify the building, and the city in which it is located.

You score one point for each correct answer. A score of 14 is passing; 18 is outstanding; and 22 indicates that you are either extremely well-read or well-traveled.

Answers on page 115

1. _ _ _ _ _ _ _ _

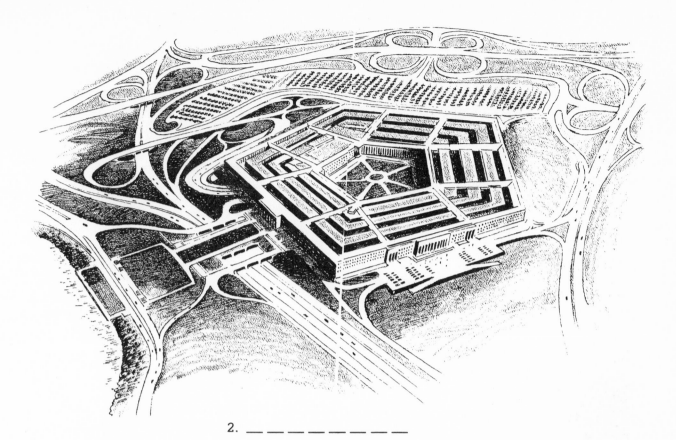

2. _ _ _ _ _ _ _ _

3. _ _ _ _ _ _ _ _

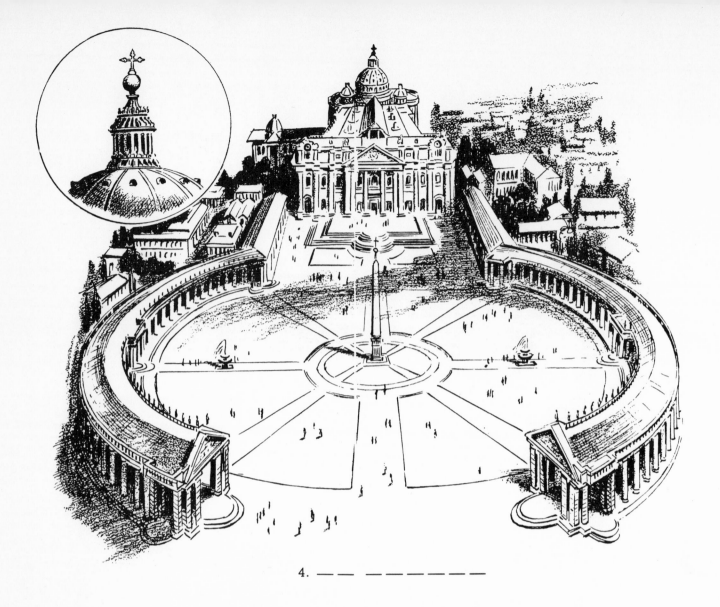

4. _ _ _ _ _ _ _ _ _

5. _ _ _ _ _ _ _ _ _ _

6. __ __ __ __ __ __   __ __ __ __ __

7. __ __ __ __ __   __ __ __ __ __

__ __ __ __ __

8. __ __ __   __ __ __ __ __

9. _ _ _ _ _ _ _ _ _ _ _ _ _

10. _ _ _ _ _ _ _ _ _ _ _ _ _

11. _ _ _ _ _ _ _ _ _ _ _ _

12. _ _ _ _ _ _ _ _ _ _
_ _ _ _ _ _ _

13. _ _ _ _ _ _ _ _ _ _ _ _ _

or _ _ _ _ _ _ _ _ _ _ _ _ _

DO YOU KNOW YOUR FLAGS

On these pages there are 20 representations of flags. Each of these flags is the emblem of a particular country. Even though the color is not shown, the pattern itself is distinctive. Can you identify the country?

A list of countries follows. Fill in the name of the country under its flag.

AUSTRALIA	LIBERIA
CANADA	NORTH KOREA
CHILE	NORWAY
CZECHOSLOVAKIA	PAKISTAN
EGYPT	PANAMA
GREAT BRITAIN	SWITZERLAND
GREECE	SYRIA
ISRAEL	TURKEY
JAMAICA	U.S.S.R.
JAPAN	YUGOSLAVIA

A score of 7 is passable; 10 is good; 12 is excellent; and 15 is exceptional.

Answers on page 115

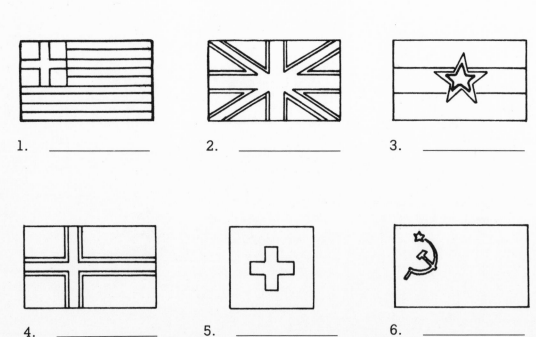

1. _____

2. _____

3. _____

4. _____

5. _____

6. _____

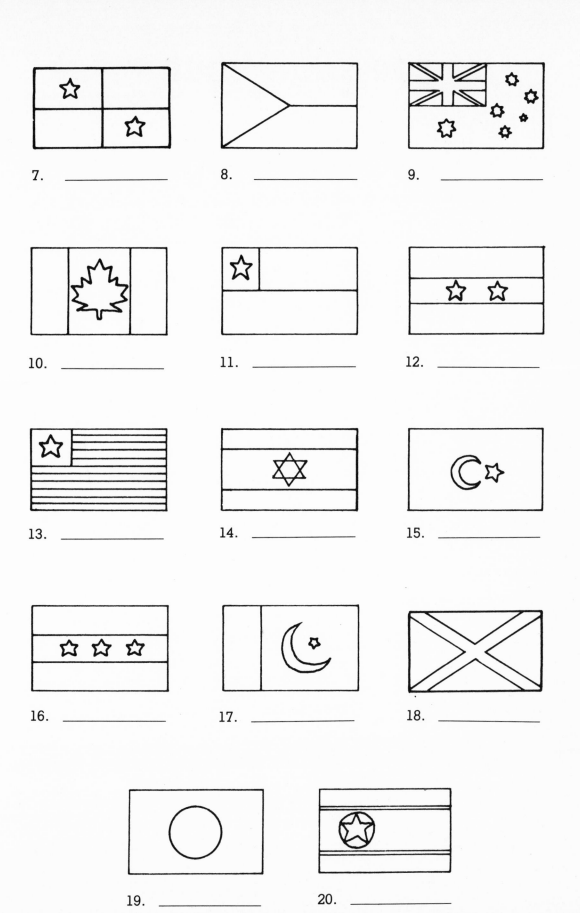

7. _____

8. _____

9. _____

10. _____

11. _____

12. _____

13. _____

14. _____

15. _____

16. _____

17. _____

18. _____

19. _____

20. _____

WELL-ARMED

Are you versed in the ways of war? All of the 20 pictures on the following pages are weapons. The dashes indicate the number of letters in each name. How many of them can you identify?

A score of 6 is good; 9 is excellent; 13 is special; 17 brands you as a weapons buff; and 19 classes you as an encyclopedist.

Answers on page 116

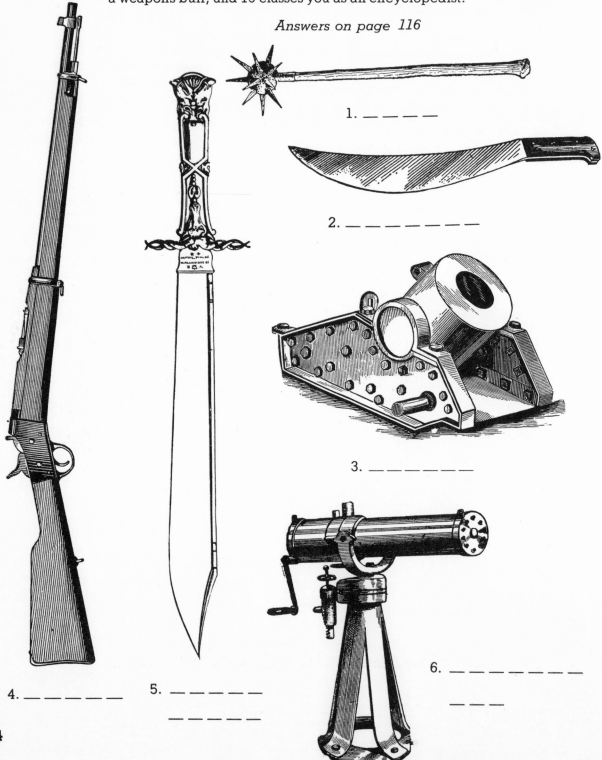

1. _ _ _ _

2. _ _ _ _ _ _

3. _ _ _ _ _ _

4. _ _ _ _ _ _

5. _ _ _ _ _
   _ _ _ _

6. _ _ _ _ _ _
   _ _ _

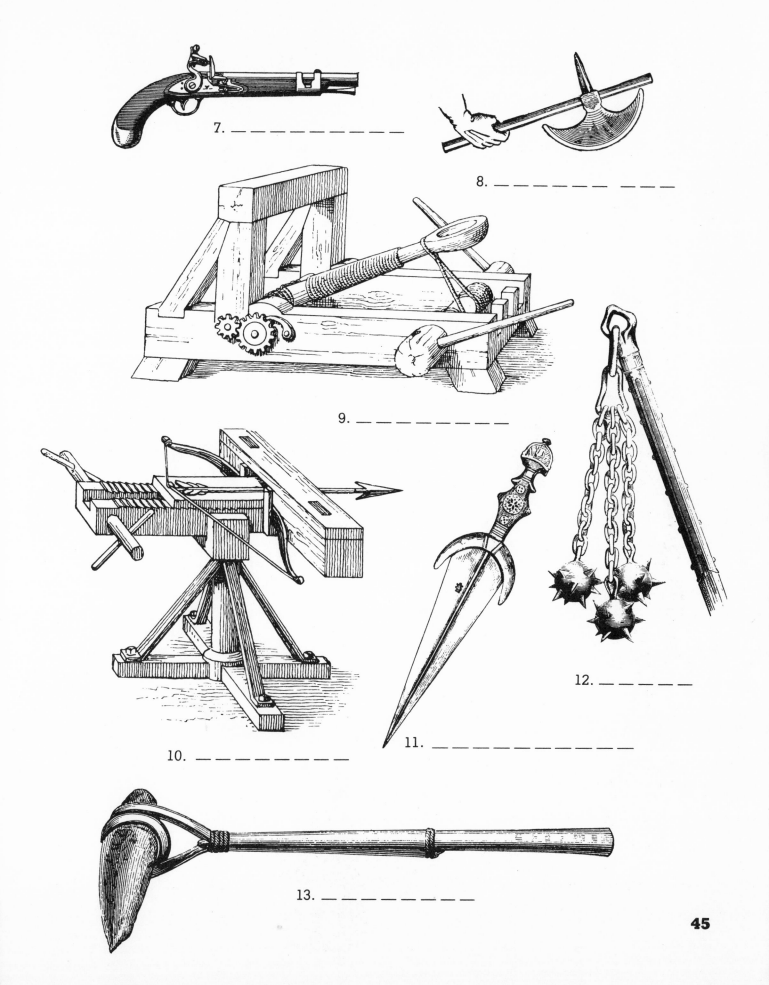

7. _ _ _ _ _ _ _ _ _

8. _ _ _ _ _ _ _ _ _

9. _ _ _ _ _ _ _ _

10. _ _ _ _ _ _ _

11. _ _ _ _ _ _ _ _ _

12. _ _ _ _ _

13. _ _ _ _ _ _ _

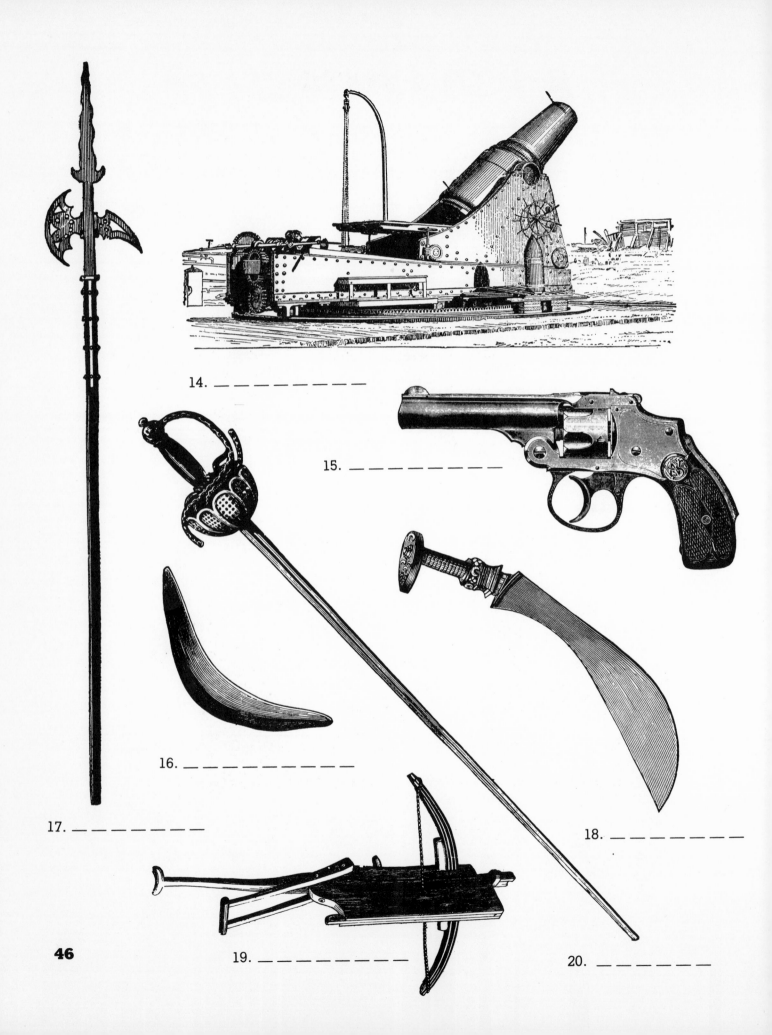

14. _ _ _ _ _ _ _

15. _ _ _ _ _ _ _

16. _ _ _ _ _ _ _

17. _ _ _ _ _ _

18. _ _ _ _ _ _

19. _ _ _ _ _ _ _

20. _ _ _ _ _

IN SUCH A STATE

Here are 16 states of the Union. Can you tell from their shapes which ones they are? Be careful—it may be harder than you think.

A score of 6 is good; 10 is excellent; 12 makes you a real statesman!

Answers on page 116

1. _____

2. _____

3. _____

4. _____

5. _____

6. _____

7. _____

8. _____

9. _____

10. _____

11. _____

12. _____

13. _____

14. _____

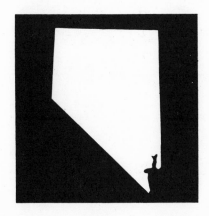

15. _____

16. _____

AMERICAN WRITERS

On the following pages you will find pictures of 16 famous American writers. The dashes under each name indicate how many letters there are in the name.

A score of 6 is passing; 8 is good; 12 is super; and 14 makes you a standout.

Answers on page 116

1. __ __ __ __
   __ __ __ __ __ __ __

2. __ __ __ __ __ __ __
   __ __ __ __ __

3. __ __ __ __ __ __ __ __ __ __ __
   __ __ __ __ __ __ __

4. _ _ _ _ _ _   _ _ _ _ _ _   _ _ _

5. _ _ _ _ _ _ _ _ _ _

_ _ _ _ _ _ _ _ _ _

6. _ _ _ _ _ _ _ _   _ _ _ _ _ _   _ _

_ _ _ _ _

7. _ _ _ _ _ _ _

_ _ _ _ _ _ _ _

10. _ _ _ _ _
    _ _ _ _ _ _ _

9. _ _ _ _ _ _
   _ _ _ _ _ _ _

8. _ _ _ _ _
   _ _ _ _ _ _ _ _ _

12. _ _ _ _
    _ _ _ _ _

11. _ _ _ _ _ _
    _ _ _ _ _ _ _ _ _

13. _ _ _ _ _
    _ _ _ _ _ _ _ _ _
    _ _ _ _ _ _ _ _ _

14. _ _ _ _ _ _ _
    _ _ _ _ _ _ _ _

15. _ _ _ _ _
    _ _ _ _ _ _

16. _ _ _ _ _ _ _ _ _ _

THEY ALL BEGIN WITH M

Each of the 21 items pictured on these pages begins with the letter M. The dashes beneath each picture indicate the number of letters in the name. Can you identify them?

A score of 10 shouldn't make you mad; 14 is mollifying; and 18 or more is magnificent.

Answers on page 116

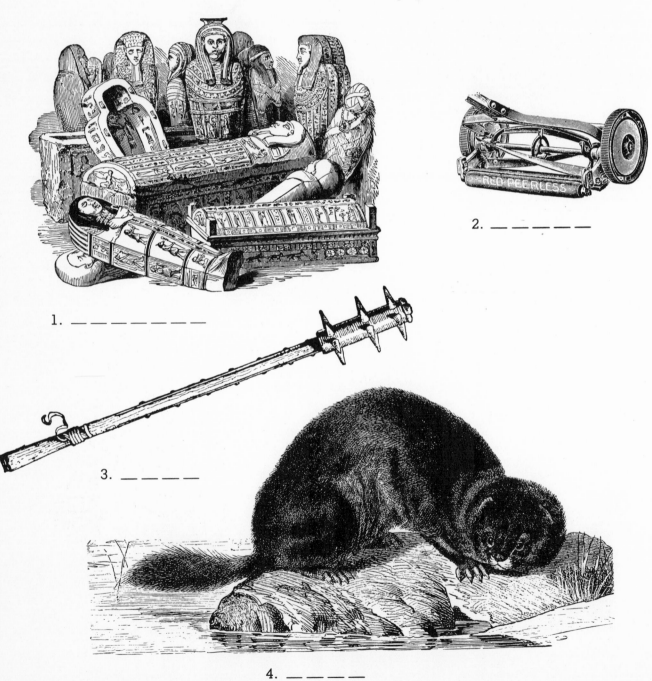

1. _ _ _ _ _ _ _

2. _ _ _ _ _ _

3. _ _ _ _ _

4. _ _ _ _ _

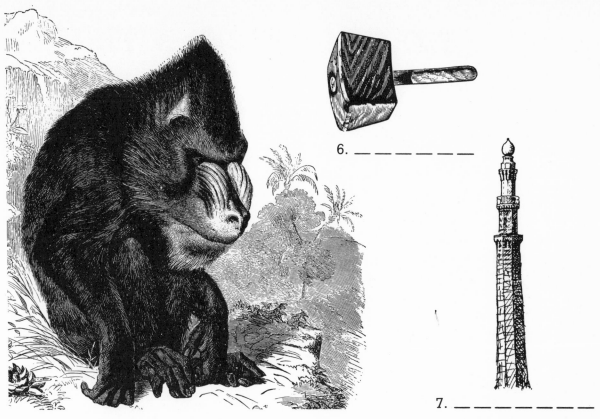

6. _ _ _ _ _ _ _ _

7. _ _ _ _ _ _ _ _

5. _ _ _ _ _ _ _ _ _

8. _ _ _ _ _ _

10. _ _ _ _ _ _ _ _ _

9. _ _ _ _ _ _ _

11. _ _ _ _ _ _ _ _

12. _ _ _ _ _ _

13. _ _ _ _ _ _ _ _ _ _ _

_ _ _ _ _ _

14. _ _ _ _ _ _ _

15. _ _ _ _ _ _ _ _ _ _

16. _ _ _ _ _ _ _ _

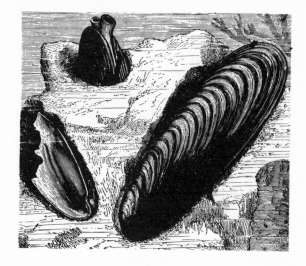

17. _ _ _ _ _ _ _

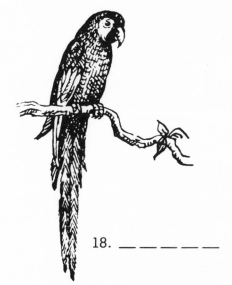

18. _ _ _ _ _ _

19. _ _ _ _

20. _ _ _ _ _ _

21. _ _ _ _ _ _ _

WHOSE ZOO?

Pictured on this and the following pages are 22 animals, some familiar, some not. Read the clue under each picture, and try to fill in the blanks, which represent the number of letters in the creature's name.

A score of 12 is good; 15 is better; and 18 is great. If you can identify all 22, you must have just returned from a safari.

Answers on page 116

1. This large and fierce cat is usually spotted. The solid black variety has given its name to a radical political group.

THIS ANIMAL IS A

— — — — — — —

2. The name of this wild dog, which feeds on carrion and hunts in packs, has become an abusive epithet for fawning followers.

THIS ANIMAL IS A

— — — — — —

3. This agile wild goat can be found on the snow line of Asian and European mountain ranges. The Alpine species is very rare.

THIS ANIMAL IS AN __ __ __ __

4. The name of this powerful carnivore is often invoked to describe a shrieking maniacal laugh.

THIS ANIMAL IS A __ __ __ __ __

5. This shy, gentle jungle herbivore has a long flexible snout. This animal stays near water, and when pursued, it plunges in.

THIS ANIMAL IS A __ __ __ __ __

6. A member of the weasel family, this maladorous mammal commonly has a thick black fur with two white stripes down the back.

THIS ANIMAL IS A __ __ __ __ __

7. The dark brown pelt of this small carnivore is so highly prized that the species is now endangered.

THIS ANIMAL IS A __ __ __ __ __

8. Also called the puma or mountain lion, this once numerous species has given its name to an American automobile.

THIS ANIMAL IS A __ __ __ __ __ __

9. The largest cat in the Americas, this yellow-and-black cousin of the leopard adorns the hood of a British automobile.

THIS ANIMAL IS A __ __ __ __ __ __

10. This slow-moving animal hangs from branches with its back downward. The sluggishness which gives it its name is one of the seven deadly sins.

THIS ANIMAL IS A __ __ __ __ __

11. The largest of all deer, this animal shares its name with a national fraternal order.

THIS ANIMAL IS AN __ __ __

12. This graceful African gazelle derives its name from the way it leaps slightly and suddenly as it runs.

THIS ANIMAL IS A

__ __ __ __ __ __ __ __ __

13. Some species of this heavily armored animal can roll themselves into a ball for protection.

THIS ANIMAL IS AN

__ __ __ __ __ __ __ __ __

14. This small carnivore shares its name with a modern French playwright.

THIS ANIMAL IS A __ __ __ __ __

15. The state animal of Wisconsin, this burrowing mammal has given its name to a particularly persistent form of pestering.

THIS ANIMAL IS A __ __ __ __ __ __

16. The largest rodent in existence—over four feet long—this aquatic native of South America is edible.

THIS ANIMAL IS A

__ __ __ __ __ __ __

17. This animal with the face mask and striped tail provides a good coat for watching a football game on a cold day.

THIS ANIMAL IS A

— — — — — — —

18. In America, this animal is known as a wolverine, but in any country, it's known for its enormous appetite.

THIS ANIMAL IS A

— — — — — — — —

19. The North American species of this wild ox was nearly eradicated in the 18th century.

THIS ANIMAL IS A

— — — — — — —

20. The first letter in the name of this large African antelope is silent.

THIS ANIMAL IS A __ __ __

21. This South American animal provides some of us with wonderful coats.

THIS ANIMAL IS A __ __ __ __ __

22. This enormous creature might scare you with its horn, but don't worry—it's a plant-eating mammal.

THIS ANIMAL IS A

— — — — — — — —

FAMOUS ATHLETES

Here are 19 pictures of athletes whom you have heard about for many years. These famous personalities excelled in diverse sports. How many of them do you recognize?

A score of 7 is good; 12 is excellent; and 16 merits a cheer.

Answers on page 116

1. _____

2. _____

3. _____

4. _____

5. _____

6. _____

7. _____

8. _____

9. _____

10. _____

11. _____

13. _____

12. _____

14. _____

64

15. _____

16. _____

17. _____

18. _____

19. _____

NOTED ACTORS AND ENTERTAINERS

On the following pages you will find the pictures of 16 actors and entertainers who have won acclaim either in our day or theirs. How many of them can you identify?

A score of 4 is passing; 6 is good; 9 is excellent; and 14 is absolutely outstanding.

Answers on page 117

1. _____   2. _____

3. _____   4. _____

66

5. _____

6. _____

7. _____

8. _____

9. _____

10. _____

11. _____

12. _____

13. _____

14. _____

15. _____

16. _____

69

AMERICAN STATESMEN

On the following pages, 16 American statesmen are pictured. You've seen pictures of these men—some on dollar bills, some on coins, some in history books. How many of them can you identify?

To help you, there is an identifying statement for each person.

A score of 4 is passing; 7 is above average; 8 is excellent; and 11 is outstanding.

Answers on page 117

He fought and won a famous duel. He was also tried for treason but acquitted.

1. _____

Confederate notable.

2. _____

Lincoln's famous debating contestant.

3. _____

Uncompromising abolitionist.

4. _____

Printer, inventor, scientist, statesman.

5. _____

First U.S. Secretary of the Treasury.

6. _____

He served as Secretary of War; then, as Vice-President until he resigned.

7. _____

Famous lawyer and gifted orator, he served as Secretary of State.

8. _____

Famous orator of the Revolution.

9. _____

His signature may be more familiar than his face.

10. _____

President who gave U.S. a New Deal

11. _____

Famous pamphleteer of the Revolution.

12. _____

Inventor of shuttle diplomacy.

13. _____

Nominated for president, he lost to McKinley.

14. _____

He ran for President as a Socialist.

15. _____

He lost the presidential election to Eisenhower.

16. _____

THEY ALL BEGIN WITH G

Below, you will see 10 pictures representing animals and objects, all of whose names begin with a G. How many can you find?

A score of 5 is passing; 6 is good; 8 is excellent; and a perfect score of 10 merits you a gold loving cup.

Answers on page 117

2. _ _ _ _ _ _ _ _ _

3. _ _ _ _ _ _ _ _

1. _ _ _ _ _ _ _ _ _ _ _

   _ _ _ _ _

4. _ _ _ _ _ _

5. _ _ _ _ _ _ _   _ _ _ _ _

6. _ _ _ _ _

7. _ _ _ _ _ _ _ _ _ _ _
   _ _ _ _ _

8. _ _ _ _ _ _ _ _

9. _ _ _ _ _ _ _

10. _ _ _ _ _ _ _

THEY ALL BEGIN WITH P

Pictured on these pages are 24 objects, each of which begins with the letter P. The dashes show how many letters are in each name. How many of these items can you identify?

A score of 9 is pretty good, 12, par excellence; and 15 plainly portrays perspicacity, and 22 is practically perfect.

Answers on page 117

2. _ _ _ _ _ _ _ _ _

3. _ _ _ _ _ _

1. _ _ _ _ _ _

4. _ _ _ _ _ _

5. _ _ _ _ _ _ _

6. _ _ _ _ _ _

7. _ _ _ _ _ _ _

8. _ _ _ _ _   _ _ _ _ _

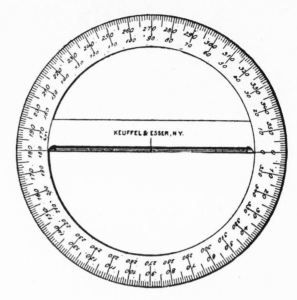

9. _ _ _ _ _ _ _ _

10. _ _ _ _ _ _ _ _

11. _ _ _ _ _ _ _ _ _

12. _ _ _ _ _ _

13. _ _ _ _ _

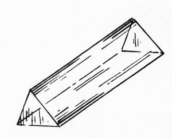

14. _ _ _ _ _ _

16. _ _ _ _ _

17. _ _ _ _

18. _ _ _ _ _ _ _

15. _ _ _ _ _ _

19. _ _ _ _ _ _ _

20. _ _ _ _ _

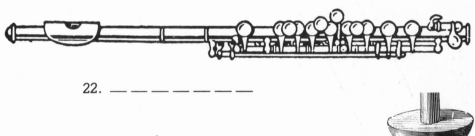

21. _ _ _ _ _

22. _ _ _ _ _

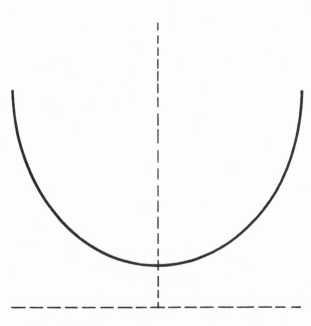

23. _ _ _ _ _

24. _ _ _ _ _

MUSIC TO MY EARS

All of the 20 objects on the following pages are musical instruments. They derive from many countries. How many of them can you identify?

A score of 6 is good; 8 is very good; 12 is terrific; 15 marks you as a student of music; and 18 says that you must be a musicologist.

Answers on page 117

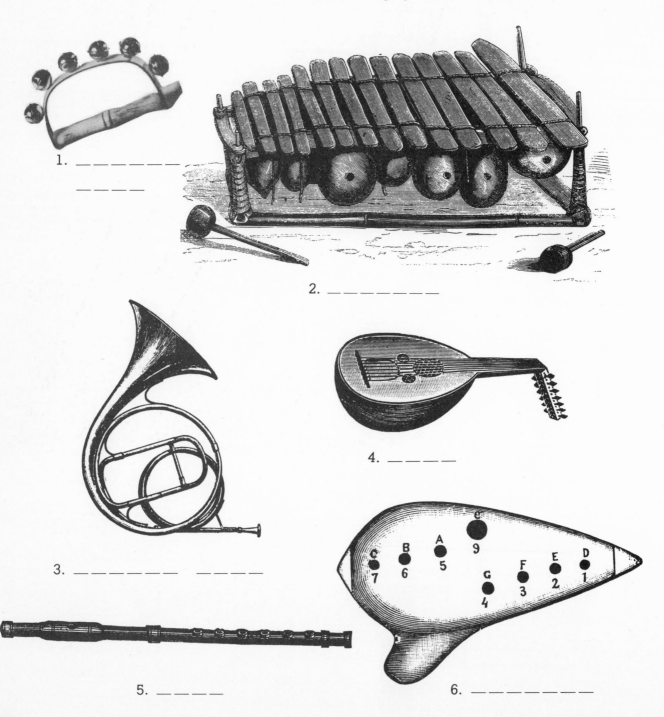

1. _ _ _ _ _ _ _ _

   _ _ _ _ _

2. _ _ _ _ _ _ _ _

3. _ _ _ _ _ _ _ _   _ _ _ _

4. _ _ _ _ _

5. _ _ _ _ _

6. _ _ _ _ _ _ _ _

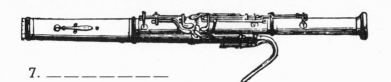

7. _ _ _ _ _ _ _ _

8. _ _ _ _ _ _ _

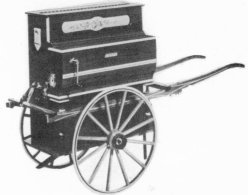

9. _ _ _ _ _ _ _ _ _

10. _ _ _ _ _ _ _ _ _

11. _ _ _ _ _ _ _ _ _ _ _

12. _ _ _ _ _ _

13. _ _ _ _ _ _ _ _ _

14. ___ ___ ___ ___

15. ___ ___ ___ ___

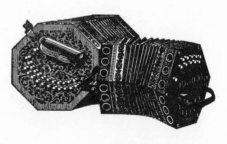

16. ___ ___ ___

17. ___ ___ ___ ___

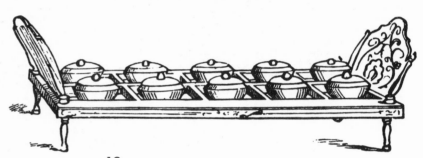

18. ___ ___ ___ ___ ___

19. ___ ___ ___ ___

20. ___ ___ ___ ___ ___

SHIP AHOY!

There are 19 boats pictured below. Many of them are strange and unusual. Others should be rather familiar. How many of them can you recognize? Each letter in the word is represented by a dash. Some of the letters have already been filled in.

A score of 6 is good; 9 is above average; 10 is excellent; and 13 is quite unusual. Anything above that figure marks you as a seafarer.

Answers on page 117

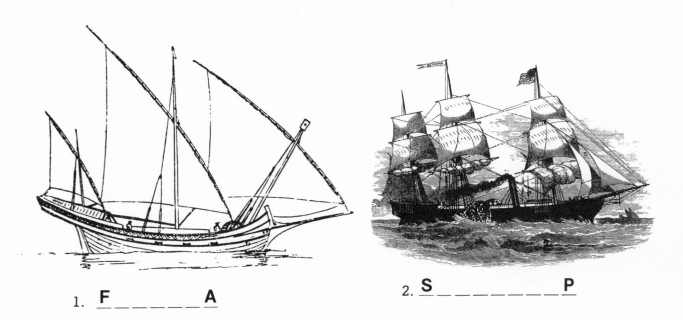

1. F _ _ _ _ A

2. S _ _ _ _ _ _ _ P

3. _ _ R _ _

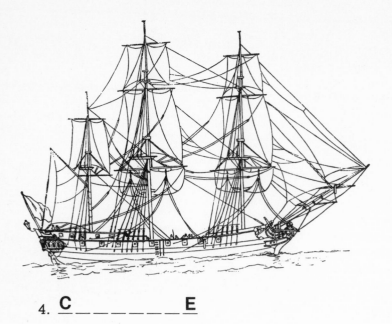

4. __C_ _ _ _ _ _ _E__

5. __D_ _ _ _ _ _ ___ _ _T__

6. __G_ _ _ _ _Y__

7. __S_ _ _ _ _ _ _ _ _ _ _ _R__

8. __C_ _ _ _E__

9. **C** _ _ _ _ _ _ **L**

10. _ _ _ _ **D** _ _ _ _

11. **I** _ _ _ _ _ _ _ _ **T**

12. _ _ _ _ **K**

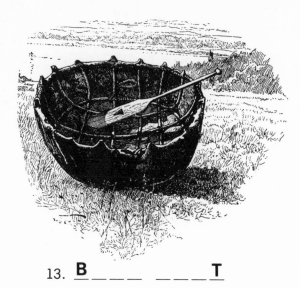

13. **B** _ _ _ _   _ _ _ _ **T**

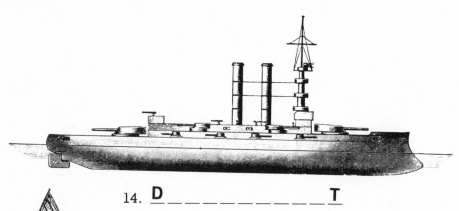

14. **D** _ _ _ _ _ _ _ _ _ _ **T**

15. **S** _ _ _ _ _ _ _ **T**

16. **F** _ _ _ _ _ _ **E**

17. **S** _ _ _ _ **P**

18. **R** _ _ _ _ _ _ **T**

19. **S** _ _ _ _ _ _ _ **T**

PLAYWRIGHTS

The 8 playwrights whose pictures you see here have entertained audiences from as far back as the 4th century B.C. to the present. A note under each picture should help you to identify the dramatist.

A score of 4 is good; 6 is very good; and 8 indicates that you are stage-struck.

Answers on page 118

This American playwright of the 1930's wrote realistic dramas with political themes.

1. _____

This Irish dramatist and noted wit wrote polished light comedy.

2. _____

A firm believer in love and life and the common man, he wrote highly winning comedy-fantasy around 1940.

3. _____

One of the great Athenian poets, he led a long and venerable life as a statesman, a public office holder, and a poet. In 471 B.C., he entered his first drama contest, and won.

4. _____

He is considered by some to be America's foremost dramatist.

5. _____

He was a Cambridge scholar, poet, and the greatest of the "University Wits." He profoundly influenced the Elizabethan theater.

6. _____

This man is the foremost English representative of the "Theater of the Absurd." His first full-length play, *The Caretaker*, written in 1960, won him acclaim on both sides of the Atlantic.

7. _____

Once a gag writer for TV, this playwright followed his first Broadway comedy hit, *Come Blow Your Horn,* written in 1962, with a string of successes that have made him a legend in his lifetime.

8. _____

THEY ALL BEGIN WITH S

On these two pages you will find 20 objects which begin with the letter S. The dashes under each picture indicate the number of letters in each name. How many can you identify?

If you correctly name 10, that's fine; 14 is super; and 18 is stupendous.

Answers on page 118

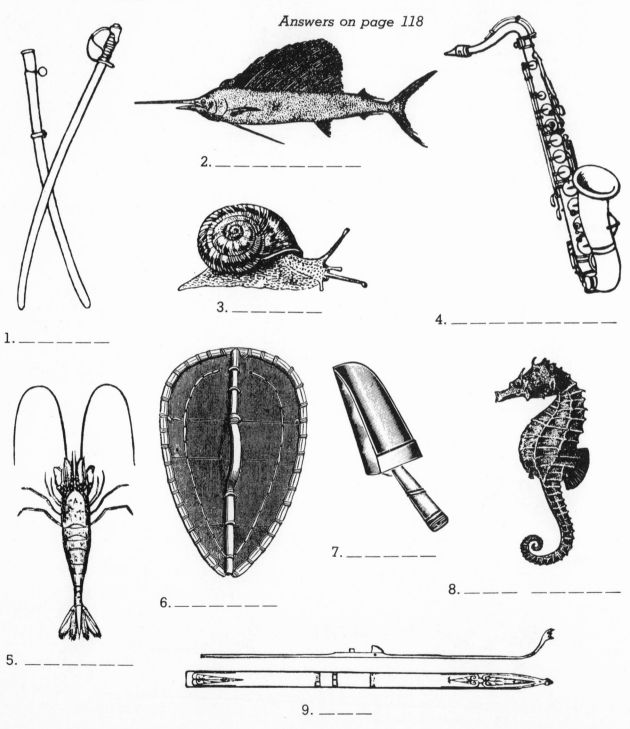

2. _ _ _ _ _ _ _ _

3. _ _ _ _ _

4. _ _ _ _ _ _ _ _ _ _

1. _ _ _ _ _ _

7. _ _ _ _ _

8. _ _ _ _   _ _ _ _ _

6. _ _ _ _ _ _ _

5. _ _ _ _ _ _ _

9. _ _ _

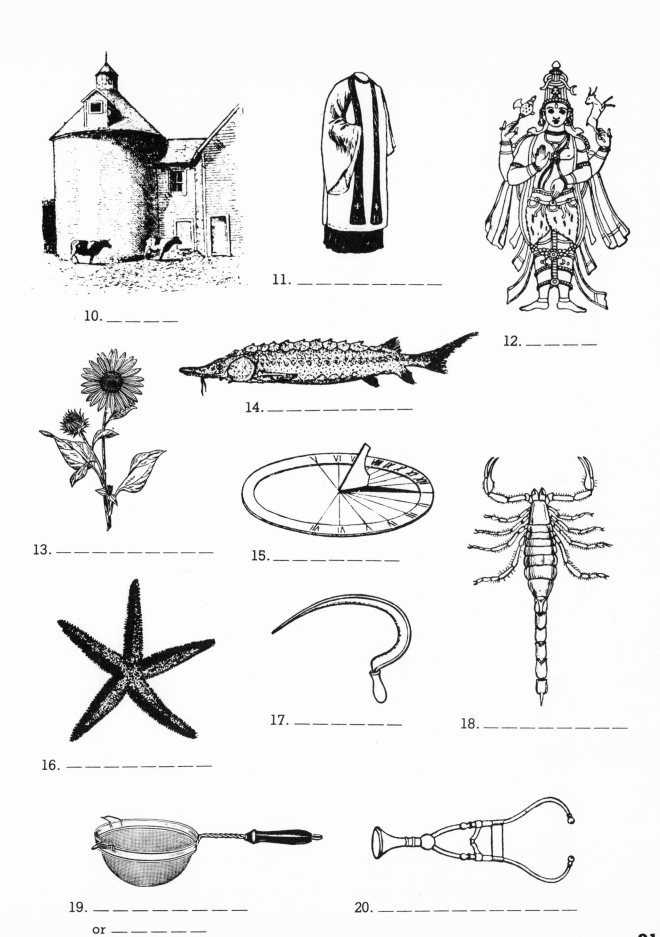

10. _ _ _ _ _

11. _ _ _ _ _ _ _ _

12. _ _ _ _ _

13. _ _ _ _ _ _ _ _ _

14. _ _ _ _ _ _ _ _

15. _ _ _ _ _ _ _

16. _ _ _ _ _ _ _

17. _ _ _ _ _ _

18. _ _ _ _ _ _ _ _

19. _ _ _ _ _ _ _ _
or _ _ _ _ _

20. _ _ _ _ _ _ _ _ _

TALL TIMBER

On these pages, you will find pictures of 10 well-known American trees. Read the clue under each picture, and see if you can come up with the name of the tree. The number of blanks corresponds to the number of letters in the tree's name.

A score of 6 is good; 8 is superior; and 10 is tree-mendous.

Answers on page 118

Also known as the plane tree, this beauty grows as high as 150 feet. Its distinctive trunk is marked by a dark outer bark which, as it ages, peels to disclose a golden bark underneath.

1. THIS TREE IS AN

— — — — — — — —
— — — — — — — —.

Originally brought over from China, this graceful tree is now common along the banks of American rivers and streams. The flexible branches make a lovely sight as they sway in the wind.

2. THIS TREE IS A

— — — — — — —
— — — — — — —.

The wood of this majestic shade tree is extremely hard; the leaves have sawtoothed edges. The tree has vanished from many towns because of a blight transmitted by bark beetles.

3. THIS TREE IS AN

— — — — — — —
— — —.

This descendant of the magnolia is named for its large flowers, which bloom in the spring and resemble Holland's famed blossoms. Its leaves are uniquely broad and squarish.

4. THIS IS A — — — — — — TREE

The fruit of this familiar tree is a large, prickly ball. It cracks open to reveal a shiny brown seed, which gives the tree its name.

5. THIS TREE IS A __ __ __ __ __
__ __ __ __ __ __ __ __.

This stately hardwood tree is used to build furniture, flooring, and railroad ties. Its acorns were cooked and eaten by American Indians.

6. THIS TREE IS A __ __ __ __ __
__ __ __.

The syrup from this lovely tree is a favorite over pancakes. The tree has a grayish bark, five-pointed leaves, and winged seed pods.

7. THIS TREE IS A __ __ __ __ __
__ __ __ __.

The needles of this fragrant tree are gathered in fanlike clusters. The wood is used to line closets and chests.

8. THIS TREE IS A __ __ __ __ __.

The large, dark nut of this tree is difficult to crack open, but the kernel is very tasty. The leaves of the tree are smooth above and hairy below.

9. THIS TREE IS A __ __ __ __ __
__ __ __ __ __ __.

Especially common in the Northeast, this tree is easily spotted by the horizontal blazes on its bark. The bark makes excellent tinder, and can even be written on.

10. THIS TREE IS A __ __ __ __ __
__ __ __ __ __.

THEY ALL BEGIN WITH T

Below, you will find 11 objects which begin with the letter T. The dashes indicate the number of letters in each name. How many can you identify?

A score of 4 is average; 8 is very good; 10 is tremendous!

Answers on page 118

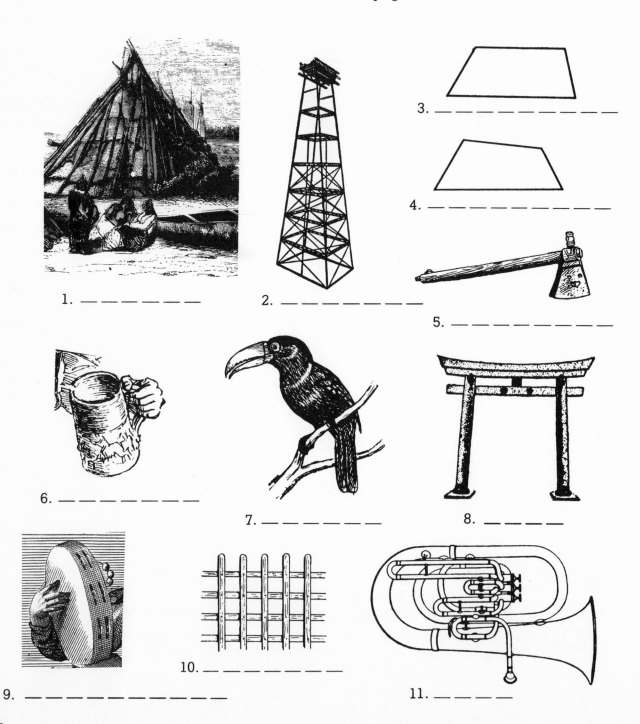

1. _ _ _ _ _ _

2. _ _ _ _ _ _ _

3. _ _ _ _ _ _ _ _

4. _ _ _ _ _ _ _

5. _ _ _ _ _ _ _ _

6. _ _ _ _ _ _

7. _ _ _ _ _ _

8. _ _ _ _ _

9. _ _ _ _ _ _ _ _

10. _ _ _ _ _ _

11. _ _ _ _

MISCELLANY

This is sort of an omnibus quiz. Here are things from the four corners of the earth. How many of these pictures can you name?

Here's your rating: 5, good; 6, very good; 7, excellent; 8, super; 9, extraordinary; 10, a man among men.

Answers on page 118

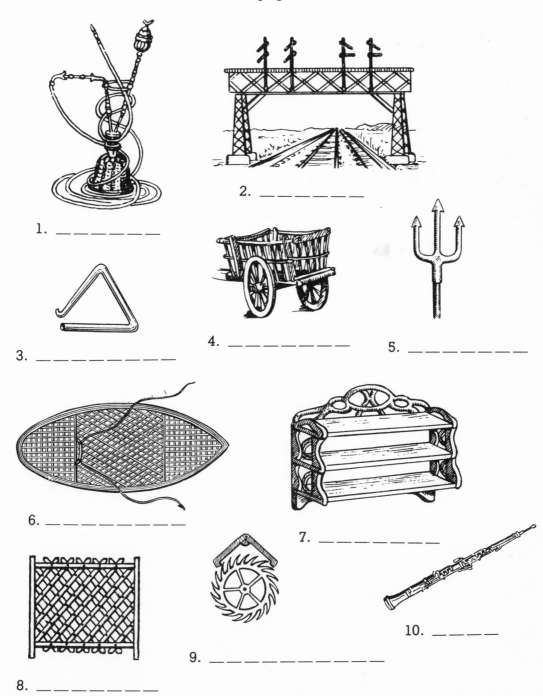

1. _ _ _ _ _ _ _

2. _ _ _ _ _ _ _

3. _ _ _ _ _ _ _ _ _

4. _ _ _ _ _ _ _

5. _ _ _ _ _ _ _ _

6. _ _ _ _ _ _ _ _

7. _ _ _ _ _ _ _ _

8. _ _ _ _ _ _ _

9. _ _ _ _ _ _ _ _ _

10. _ _ _ _ _

ARCHITECTURAL ELEMENTS

Each of the 17 objects on the following pages is a term used in architecture. Each dash represents a letter in the name. The initial letter has been provided. Can you identify the pictures?

A score of 6 is good; 8 is very good; 9 is far above average; and 15 classes you as an expert.

Answers on page 118

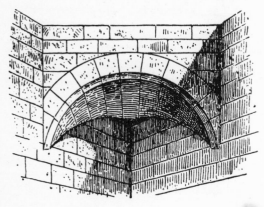

1. S _ _ _ _ _ _ _

2. T _ _ _ _ _ _ _ _

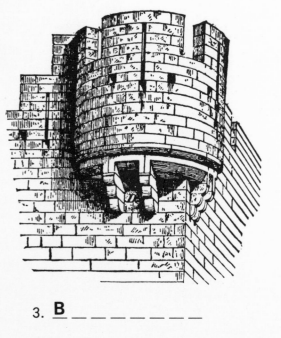

3. B _ _ _ _ _ _ _ _

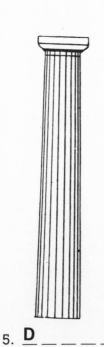

4. I _ _ _ _ _

5. D _ _ _ _ _

6. **C** _ _ _ _ _ _ _ _

7. **A** _ _ _ _ _ _ _

8. **P** _ _ _ _ _ _ _ _ _

9. **B** _ _ _ _ _ _ _ _ _

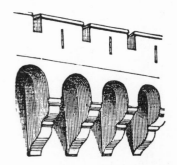

10. **F** _ _ _ _ _ _ _ _ _ _ _

11. **M** _ _ _ _ _ _

_ _ _ _ _ _ _ _

12. **V** _ _ _ _ _

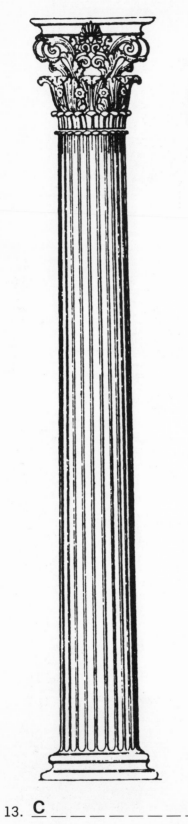

13. **C** _ _ _ _ _ _ _ _ _ _

14. **B** _ _ _ _ _ _ _

16. **P** _ _ _ _

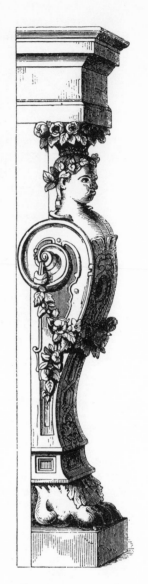

15. **C** _ _ _ _ _ _ _ _ _

17. **C** _ _ _ _ _ _ _ _ _

FOR OLD TIMERS

Below you will find a number of emblems used as trademarks by American manufacturers. How many of these companies can you identify? Some of these symbols are still in use today. Some go back a century.

A score of 2 is passing; 3 is good; 4 is excellent; and 5 is above average. A score of 6 simply indicates that you're over 60, and particularly observant.

Answers on page 118

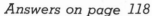

1. _____

2. _____

3. _____

4. _____

5. _____

6. _____

7. _____

8. _____

9. _____

10. _____

BIRD'S THE WORD

On the following pages there is an aviary of 19 birds. Many of these are common birds which you have seen again and again. Others are rare. How many of these birds can you identify?

To help you, the dashes under each picture indicates how many letters there are in the name. Some filled in letters will help.

A score of 6 is passing; 8 is above average; 11 is excellent; 14 is outstanding; and 17 brands you as a bird watcher.

Answers on page 119

1. M _ _ _ _ _ _ G _ _ _

2. P _ _ _ _ _ T

3. S _ _ _ _

4. C _ _ _ _ _ _ L

5. **H** _ _ _ _ _ **D O** _ _

6. _ _ _ _ _ **O W** _ _ _ _ _

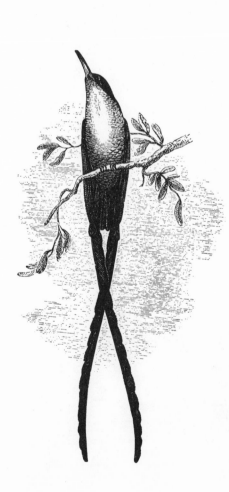

8. **B L** _ _ _ _ _ _ _

7. **H** _ **M** _ _ _ _ _ _ _

9. _ _ _ _ **K**

101

11. _ _ _ _ **P P** _ _ _ _ _ **L L**

10. **P** _ _ _ _ _ _ **K**

12. **P** _ _ _ _ _ _ **T**

13. **G** _ _ _ _ _ _

14. _ _ _ _ _ _ **Y**

15. **P H** _ _ _ _ _ _ _ _

16. **H** _ _ _ _

17. _ _ _ _ _ _ **R** _ **W**

18. _ _ _ _ _ _ _ **O O**

19. **D** _ _ _ _

THE CELEBRATED
AND THE NOTORIOUS

On the following pages, you will find the pictures of 36 people, all of whom you have heard about. Their faces have appeared in periodicals, on TV, and in books. How many of these persons can you identify?

A score of 8 is passing; 12 is good; 16 is excellent; 20 puts you far above average; and 26 says that you are positively exceptional.

Answers on page 119

1. _____

2. _____

3. _____

4. _____

5. _____

6. _____

8. _____

7. _____

9. _____

11. _____

12. _____

10. _____

13. _____

/14. _____

15. _____

16. _____

17. _____

18. _____

19. _____

20. _____

21. _____

22. _____

23. _____

24. _____

25. _____

26. _____

27. _____

28. _____

29. _____

30. _____

31. _____

32. _____

33. _____

34. _____

35. _____

36. _____

PARTS OF THE WHOLE

On the following pages, you will find 35 pictures—or more accurately, *parts* of the pictures. It is up to you to figure out what the full picture is. The full picture is in the answer section.

You score one point for every correct answer. A score of 14 is average, 20 is very good, and 25 is exceptional.

Answers on page 119

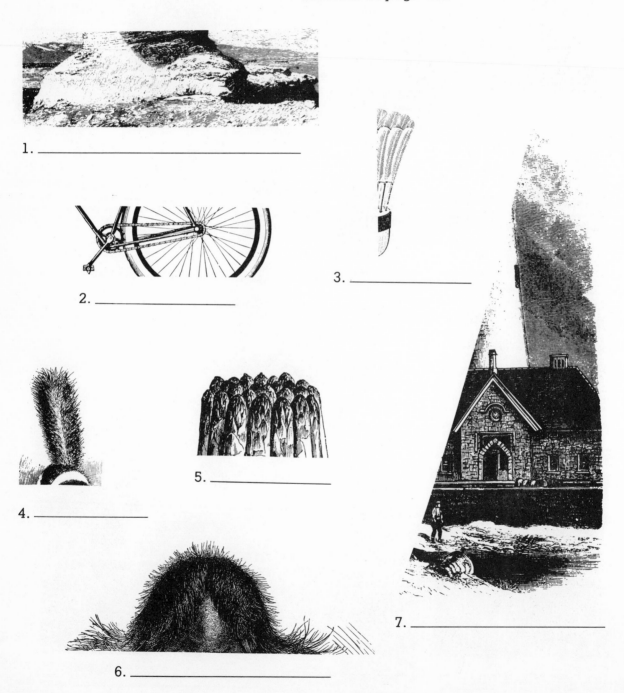

1. _____

2. _____

3. _____

4. _____

5. _____

6. _____

7. _____

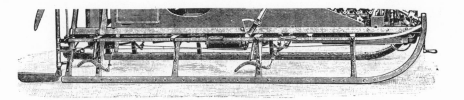

8. _____

9. _____

10. _____

12. _____

11. _____

13. _____

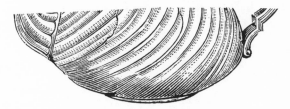

14. _____

15. _____

16. _____

17. _____

18. _____

19. _____

20. _____

21. _____

22. _____

23. _____

24. _____

25. _____

26. _____

27. _____

28. _____

29. _____

30. _____

31. _____

32. _____

33. _____

34. _____

35. _____

THE ANSWERS

THEY ALL BEGIN WITH C . . . . . . page 8

1. Cheetah
2. Cradle
3. Candelabrum
4. Chinchilla
5. Cornet
6. Cauliflower
7. Crane
8. Coyote
9. Chariot
10. Cameo

THEY ALL BEGIN WITH F . . . . . page 10

1. Flagon
2. Fox
3. Flute
4. Fly
5. Faun
6. Fedora
7. Forceps
8. Fir
9. Flounder
10. Falcon
11. Ferret

THEY ALL BEGIN WITH H . . . . . page 12

1. Hare
2. Harpoon
3. Heron
4. Hammock
5. Harmonica
6. Harp
7. Honeycomb
8. Hyena
9. Hedgehog

SIGNIFICANT INSIGNIA . . . . page 14

1. Little League
2. Rotary Club
3. American Medical Association
4. Masons
5. Cadillac
6. Red Men
7. Pontaic
8. Camp Fire Girls
9. National Association for the Advancement of Colored People
10. Lions Club
11. Boy Scouts of America
12. Young Men's Christian Association
13. Knights of Columbus
14. St. Louis Cardinals
15. U.S. Coast Guard
16. International Workers of the World
17. Oldsmobile

THEY ALL BEGIN WITH B . . . . . page 17

1. Boxing gloves
2. Bagpipe
3. Brig
4. Beetle
5. Barracuda
6. Breastplate
7. Basket
8. Bugle
9. Balustrade
10. Bonnet
11. Bighorn
12. Bison
13. Bumblebee
14. Bolo
15. Buskins
16. Binoculars

NOTED ACTRESSES . . . . page 20

1. Elizabeth Taylor
2. Doris Day
3. Marilyn Miller
4. Sarah Bernhardt
5. Bette Davis
6. Hedy Lamarr
7. Lauren Bacall
8. Marilyn Monroe
9. Faye Dunaway
10. Dorothy Lamour

YE GODS! . . . . page 22

1. Triton
2. Fury
3. Siva
4. Pan
5. Helios
6. Apis
7. Bacchus
8. Nebo
9. Isis
10. Ariadne
11. Hades
12. Ceres
13. Athena
14. Medusa
15. Thor
16. Artemis
17. Mercury
18. Osiris
19. Seth
20. Ganymede

13. Nadia Comaneci
14. Muhammad Ali
15. Babe Ruth
16. Bjorn Borg
17. Bobby Jones
18. Rogers Hornsby
19. Babe Didrikson Zaharias

NOTED ACTORS AND ENTERTAINERS . . . . page 66

1. Richard Burton
2. Charles Chaplin
3. Fred Astaire
4. Mort Sahl
5. Laurence Olivier
6. John Barrymore
7. Dustin Hoffman
8. Edwin Booth
9. James Dean
10. Sabu
11. John Gielgud
12. Humphrey Bogart
13. Ralph Richardson
14. Burt Lancaster
15. Charles Bronson
16. John Drew

AMERICAN STATESMEN . . . . . . page 70

1. Aaron Burr
2. Jefferson Davis
3. Stephen Douglas
4. William Lloyd Garrison
5. Benjamin Franklin
6. Alexander Hamilton
7. John Calhoun
8. Daniel Webster
9. Patrick Henry
10. John Hancock
11. Franklin D. Roosevelt
12. Thomas Paine
13. Henry Kissinger
14. William Jennings Bryan
15. Norman Thomas
16. Adlai Stevenson

THEY ALL BEGIN WITH G . . . . . page 74

1. Grandfather clock
2. Gauntlet
3. Gondola
4. Goblet
5. Guinea pigs
6. Goat
7. Grappling hook
8. Guitar
9. Gopher
10. Garter

THE ALL BEGIN WITH P . . . . page 76

1. Pagoda
2. Periscope
3. Parka
4. Pincers
5. Palette
6. Pistol
7. Parsnip
8. Palm tree
9. Protractor
10. Pelican
11. Palinquin
12. Plane
13. Pacon
14. Prism
15. Peacock
16. Plow
17. Pigs
18. Platypus
19. Pitchfork
20. Pillory
21. Piano
22. Piccolo
23. Parabola
24. Pulley

MUSIC TO MY EARS . . . . page 80

1. Handle bell
2. Marimba
3. French horn
4. Lute
5. Fife
6. Ocarina
7. Bassoon
8. Cymbals
9. Hurdy gurdy
10. Tom-tom
11. Chinese gong
12. Guitar
13. Trombone
14. Harmonica
15. Organ
16. Tuba
17. Violin
18. Gamelan
19. Cornet
20. Concertina

SHIP AHOY! . . . . page 83

1. Felucca
2. Steamship
3. Barge
4. Corvette
5. Double boat
6. Galley
7. Square rigger
8. Canoe
9. Caravel
10. Gondola

1.

2.

6.

9.

5.

11.

4.

7.

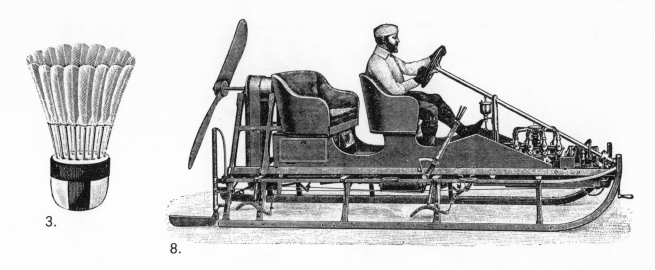

3.

8.

13.

10.

12.

15.

17.

16.

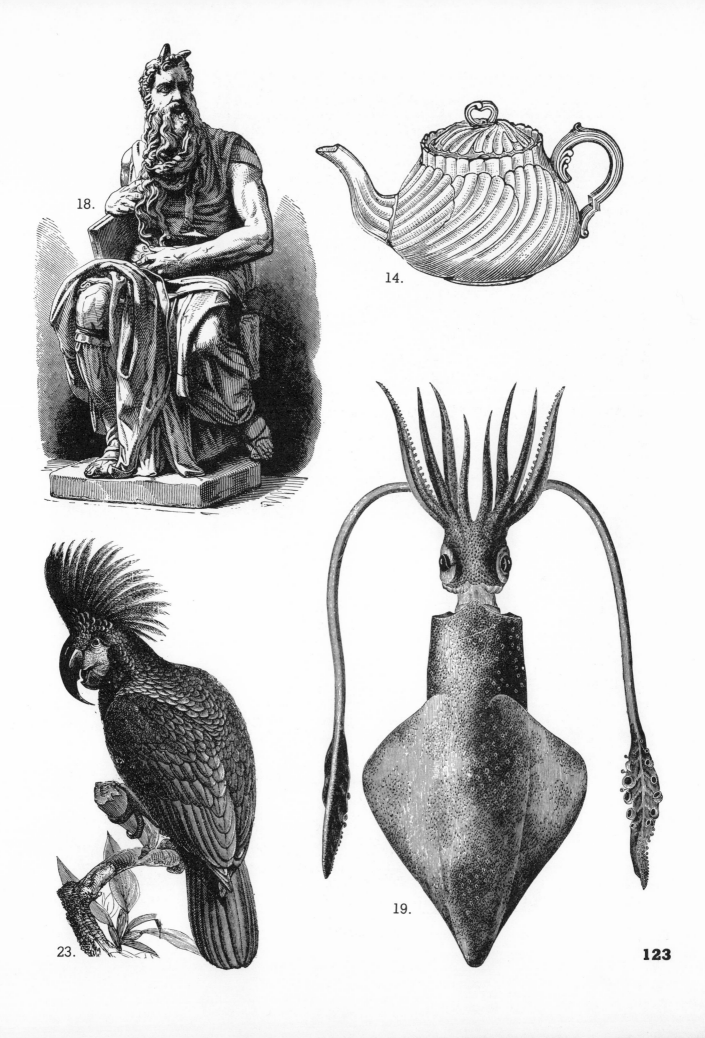

18.

14.

19.

23.

123

20.

28.

31.

22.

124

21.

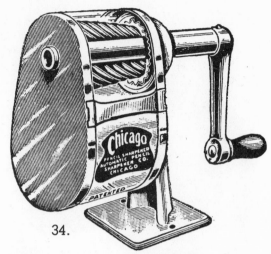

34.

25.

30.

27.

125

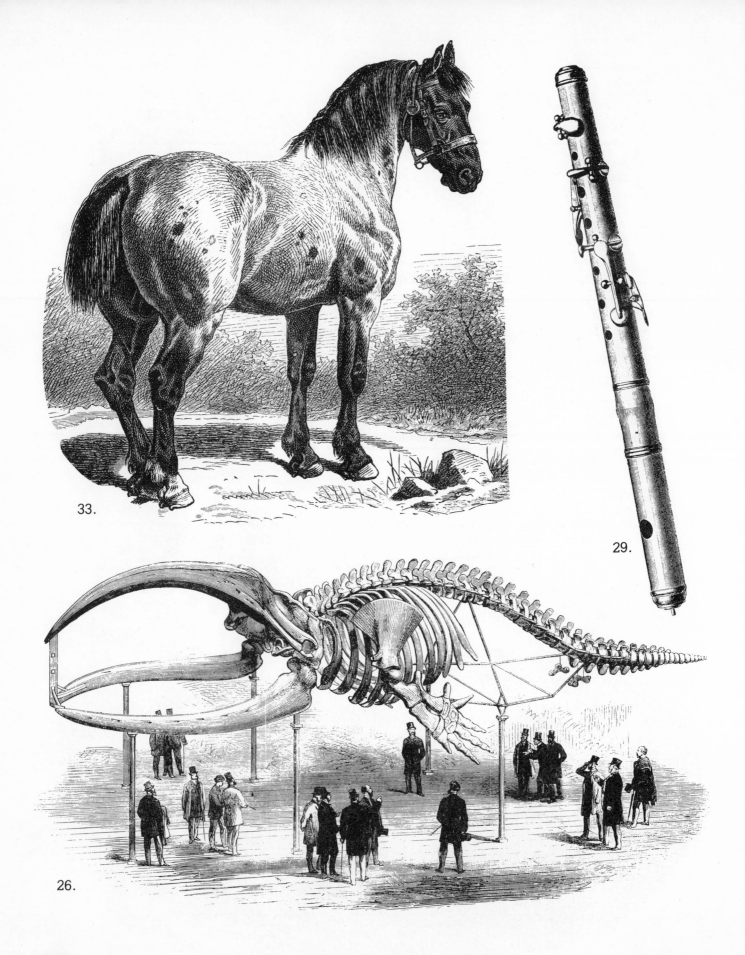

33.

29.

26.

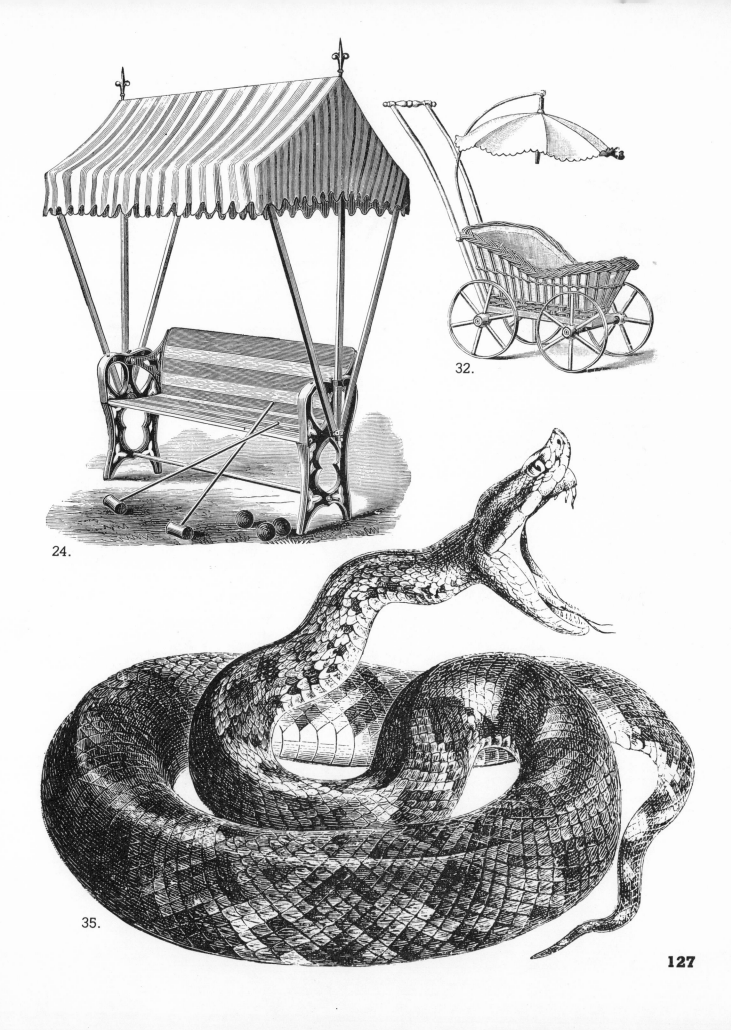

24.

32.

35.

A HART BOOK